NETWORKS

FIND A WAY BACK

John McInnes, *Senior Author*

John Ryckman

NELSON CANADA

© Nelson Canada,
A Division of International Thomson Limited, 1987

All rights in this book are reserved

Published in 1987 by
Nelson Canada,
A Division of International Thomson Limited
1120 Birchmount Road
Scarborough, Ontario
M1K 5G4

ISBN 0-17-602473-5

Canadian Cataloguing in Publication Data

McInnes, John, 1927-
    Find a Way Back

(Networks)

ISBN 0-17-602473-5

1. Readers (Primary). I. Ryckman, John, 1928-
II. Title. III. Series: Networks (Toronto, Ont.)

PE1119.M2534 1987   428.6   C86-094772-6

Printed and bound in Canada

Contents

Neighbourhood Friends

Around the corner, across the street,
Things to do, people to meet,
A place to belong—that's my neighbourhood.

Neighbours

A neighbour is someone
who takes you along
when he goes to the football game.

A neighbour is someone
who never forgets
to bring you ice cream
when you're sick.

A neighbour is someone
who throws back your ball
when it lands in his yard
by mistake.

A neighbour is someone
who teaches you how
to feed roosters and hens
at the farm.

A neighbour is someone
who helps you look for your cat
when it wanders away.

A neighbour is someone
who lends you a pump
when your bicycle has a flat tire.

A neighbour is someone
who makes you feel good
when you do something
thoughtful for her.

A Sidewalk Story

Kim and her mother were taking Champ for a walk around the neighbourhood. They came to a place that used to be a parking lot. Now there was a high board fence around it. All kinds of sounds came from behind the fence.

A man in a yellow hard hat was cutting a square hole in the fence.

"Why is he doing that?" asked Kim.

"He's making a hole for people to look through," Kim's mother said.

Kim said, "Lift me up, Mom. I want to be the first to look through the hole."

Kim's mother lifted her up.

Kim was amazed. The parking lot was gone.
Now there was a big hole in the ground. All kinds
of big machines were scooping up the earth and
dumping it into trucks.

Kim's mother set her down and continued to look through the hole.

Kim and Champ were getting impatient. "Hey Mom," Kim said. "How come there isn't a hole for kids to look through?"

"I don't know," said Kim's mother. "Let's ask the man in the hard hat."

They talked to the man, and he cut a second hole in the fence in just the right spot for children.

"Thanks!" said Kim.

"Woof!" barked Champ. The dog stood on his hind legs. He wanted to look through the hole, too.

Kim lifted up the dog.

The man in the yellow hard hat said to Kim, "I guess we need another hole in the fence."

Before you could say "bulldozer," the man sawed a third hole in the fence in just the right spot for dogs.

"Woof!" barked Champ, as if to say, "That's much better!"

"Let's get going now," said Kim's mother. "We can take another look when we walk back home."

"Okay, Mom," said Kim.

They went on their way.

Sidewalk Super

by Virginia Schonborg

There are holes
In the fence
For people
With long legs,
With short legs.
I look through
Way down below.
I see a red crane working,
I see orange hats shining,
I see a biting yellow steam shovel,
Gnawing out the earth and rock.

Every day I come
And look through
Way down below.
I see it change
From a shadowy hole
To a steel scaffold,
To a shining building.
I'm a sidewalk super!

The First Time I Heard Snow

by Lauren Wolk

Mr. Franklin lives down the street from me. He has a beautiful dog named Pilot. She goes everywhere with Mr. Franklin, walking one step ahead, leading the way.

Yesterday, when I was walking home from school, I saw Mr. Franklin and Pilot up ahead of me. I was having fun sliding down the icy sidewalks. But then I guess I went too fast, because I fell and almost slid right into Mr. Franklin. When I got up and brushed myself off, I wondered whether he was having trouble staying on his feet, too.

"Hello, Mr. Franklin. Hello, Pilot," I said.

"Hello, Toby," he said.

"How did you know it was me?" I asked.

He smiled and said, "I know your voice, of course."

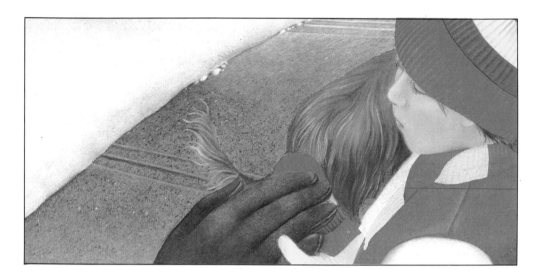

"Oh," I said. I was quite surprised. There were lots of kids in our neighbourhood. Their voices sounded pretty much the same to me.

"I wonder if you'd walk with me," said Mr. Franklin. "Pilot can't tell me where the icy patches are."

"Sure," I said. "Do you want me to take your hand?"

"It might be a good idea," said Mr. Franklin. "That way I can help you stay on your feet, too."

So I took Mr. Franklin's hand, and Pilot walked just a little ahead. As we were walking, I spotted an icy patch on the sidewalk. I thought I should warn Mr. Franklin.

"Icy patch coming up," I said. We shuffled together across the hard, smooth ice and continued our walk.

Soon, I saw the corner of our street just ahead. As far as I could see, the sidewalk was dry.

"We're almost at our corner, Mr. Franklin," I said. "And there's no more ice up ahead."

"Good," said Mr. Franklin. "You can run on home, if you want to. I'll be fine now."

"I'd rather walk with you, if that's okay," I said.

"Sure it is," said Mr. Franklin.

As we walked along, I noticed leaves blowing in the wind, birds hopping on the snow, and squirrels swinging through the branches. They made me think about all the things that Mr. Franklin couldn't see.

As I was thinking about Mr. Franklin, I heard him say, "The geese are heading south."

His voice startled me. When I looked around, I couldn't see any geese. Finally I said, "How do you know?"

"Listen," Mr. Franklin said.

I stopped walking and listened. "I can't hear any geese," I said.

"Close your eyes and listen carefully," said Mr. Franklin.

I closed my eyes and listened hard. After a few minutes, I could hear the geese honking far, far away. When I opened my eyes and looked at the sky, I saw them. They were tiny dots forming a V.

"Toby," whispered Mr. Franklin. "Have you noticed that it's snowing?"

I hadn't noticed, but now I saw that it was snowing—just a little.

"How did you know?" I asked.

"I can feel it, but I can hear it, too," whispered Mr. Franklin. "Listen."

We stopped. I listened hard.

After a few minutes had passed and I still hadn't heard anything, Mr. Franklin said, "Close your eyes. Then you will be able to hear better."

I closed my eyes. Then I thought I heard something. It was the icy snow making a sound when it hit the ground—just a little sound, hardly anything at all. But with my eyes closed, I heard it. I looked up at Mr. Franklin. He was smiling.

"You'd better hurry home now," said Mr. Franklin. "Your mother is back from work."

"How do you know?" I cried.

"Listen," he whispered.

I heard a car door slam. I heard footsteps, too. Mom's shoes always made that fast, clicking noise on the driveway. I heard the jingle of her keys, and the creak of the mailbox being opened.

"You know what, Mr. Franklin," I said. "You can hear a lot of things when you really listen!"

"That's right," said Mr. Franklin. "I think I can even hear you smiling!"

The World of Bears

There are many different kinds of bears.
They come in different sizes, shapes, and colours.
They live in many parts of the world.

All Kinds of Bears

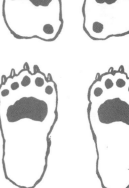

North America

Kodiak Bears

The largest bears in the world are Kodiak or "big brown" bears. Fully grown, they measure three metres from nose to tail.

Like most brown bears, Kodiaks have thick, shaggy fur. Their colour can vary from golden brown, to dark brown, to almost black. They have a hump on their shoulders. When Kodiak bears stand up on their back legs, they look enormous.

Kodiak bears eat anything, from blueberries to dead animals. But their favourite food is fish, especially salmon.

Alaska and Northwest Canada are the areas where Kodiak bears are found.

Polar Bears

Polar bears live in the Far North, where winter is long and cold. They wander the frozen seas alone, looking for animals and birds to eat. In warmer weather, they live along the seashore.

Two layers of fur protect polar bears from the cold Arctic weather. A thick undercoat keeps them warm. A smooth outer coat keeps water and snow from sticking to their fur.

Polar bears have large, furry paws and short, curved claws. They can walk on snow and ice without slipping and without making a sound. They have webbed toes that help them swim quickly.

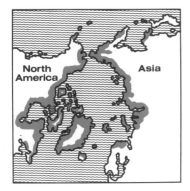

Polar bears are clever hunters. When one sees a seal sleeping on the ice, it crouches down and creeps up on the seal quietly. A polar bear will also wait at a hole in the frozen sea until a seal comes up for air. They will even hop on ice floes to hunt an animal.

Black Bears

Black bears are smaller than polar bears or brown bears. They grow to be about two metres in length. Their smooth, shiny fur is usually black, but it can also be brownish or yellowish in colour.

Black bears have short, sharp claws that make them better tree-climbers than brown bears. They scurry up trees when they are frightened, and sometimes to sleep or to find food.

A good sense of smell and good eyesight help black bears find the plants, berries, insects, and  small animals they like to eat. For a treat, black bears raid beehives for honey. Their thick fur protects them from bee stings.

Black bears can be found all over North America.

Sun Bears

The smallest of all bears are the Malayan sun bears of Southeast Asia. Their fur is smooth and black, except for a yellow, sun-like patch on their chests. Their bowed legs, long claws, and strong bodies make them good tree-climbers.

In the daytime, sun bears sleep in trees. At night, they hunt there for honey, fruit, and the soft stems of palms. Sun bears have long tongues to help them suck fruit and lick up termites.

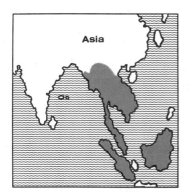

Asia

Sloth Bears

Sloth bears are small, woolly, black bears with yellowish snouts and chest markings. They make their homes in the jungles of Sri Lanka and India.

On hot days, they sleep in cool, rocky caves. At night, they hunt in the trees for fruit, honey, and birds' eggs.

Sloth bears use their strong claws to tear apart dead trees to find bugs. They especially like termites. The bears use their long snouts to suck the termites right out of their nests. The sucking sound is so loud, the bears can be heard from far away.

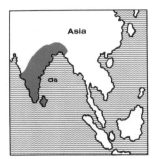

Asia

Going Fishing

The big brown bear padded through the woods. Her two cubs were right behind her. From time to time, they stopped to gather great mouthfuls of leaves, insects, and wild berries. They were headed for the river, where the big brown bears gathered to fish every summer.

Dozens of bears were already at the river. The giant male bears arrived first and took the best spots. The smaller female bears and cubs arrived later and took the places that were left. The bears stood on the rocks and in the water, waiting and watching for salmon.

The mother bear waded into the shallow water. Her two cubs waited on shore. They would learn how to fish by watching their mother and the other bears. Some day, they would try to catch their own fish.

The mother bear stood very still. All at once, she saw a big, fat salmon swimming in front of her. With a swipe of her powerful paw, she lifted the salmon out of the water and tossed it up on the shore. The two young cubs pounced on the fish and began to eat it.

Not far away, another brown bear had a different way of fishing. He stood on a rock. When he saw a fish, he would bellyflop into the water and pin the fish to the riverbed with his long, sharp claws. Then he would eat it.

One young bear caught her first fish. Another bear tried to take it from her. The young bear dove into the water to escape. She swam away quickly with the fish in her mouth.

The mother bear fished for salmon for many hours. She tossed some to her two cubs, and she ate some herself. When the cubs were not eating, they waited and watched and played with the other cubs.

At last, the mother bear climbed out of the water. She headed back to the woods with a big salmon in her mouth. This time, three cubs followed her. The third cub would stay with his new family until his own mother came to claim him.

Bubba and Babba

by Maria Polushkin

Part One: Two Lazy Bears

This is the story of two very lazy bears. One bear was named Bubba and the other was called Babba. They were so lazy that they argued all day long about who was to do what.

When they got up in the morning, Bubba said to Babba, "You must make the beds this morning, for I made them yesterday."

Babba said, "What is the point of making the beds, when in the evening we must unmake them? But Bubba, today you must sweep the floor, because I did it yesterday."

"Why should I sweep the floor when it will only get dirty again? Why don't we just leave it as it is?"

Bubba and Babba didn't make the beds and
they didn't sweep the floor, but went out for a
walk in the warm sunshine.

When the bears got home from their walk, Bubba said, "I am getting quite hungry from all that exercise."

"Yes, I am too," said Babba. "Now the sun is setting and it is getting cold. I am afraid that one of us will have to make supper and one of us will have to chop wood for a fire."

As they could think of no way to get around doing these chores, Bubba went to chop some wood and Babba cooked some porridge for their supper.

After the bears had eaten the porridge, Bubba sat back, wiped his mouth and said, "That was quite delicious, Babba. Now I will sit in front of our lovely fire while you clean up the dishes."

Babba said, "You will do nothing of the kind, Bubba. I made this porridge and by all rights you must clean up the dishes."

"My dear Babba, you are all wrong," said Bubba. "For while you were cooking, I chopped all this wood and that was a much harder job. So you must do the cleaning up."

"Bubba, you are being quite unfair and most unpleasant," said Babba. "*Everyone* knows that the one who cooks should not have to do the dishes. So please stop arguing and do them."

"I will not. You will," said Bubba.

"I most certainly will not. You will," shouted Babba.

"I will not. YOU WILL!" screamed Bubba.

"NO! YOU WILL!" shouted Babba.

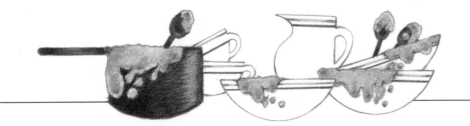

The bears shouted at each other for a long time, but neither one would give in. After a while they sat down and just looked at each other.

Finally Babba said, "I HAVE AN IDEA! Let's leave the dishes tonight and go to bed. Whoever gets up first in the morning and is the first to speak will wash the dishes."

Bubba thought that was a great idea, and they went happily off to bed.

Part Two: A Surprise Visit

When the sun came up the next morning, it was a beautiful warm day. But inside the bears' house no one stirred. Bubba and Babba lay in their beds and pretended to be asleep, for neither one wanted to be the first to get up.

The morning went by and now the sun was high overhead. Every once in a while, Bubba would peek through his tightly shut eyes to see if Babba was stirring, but Babba was lying just as quietly as Bubba.

The afternoon went by, and though it was now quite late, the two lazy bears were still in bed pretending to be asleep.

Suddenly there was a knock on the door. It was Raccoon, come to pay the bears a visit. When he knocked again and there was no answer, he decided to come in and leave them a note.

Raccoon walked into the kitchen and saw last night's dirty dishes lying on the table. "Ugh. What a mess," he said. "I think I will surprise them and clean it all up. Perhaps by the time I'm done, they will return."

Both Bubba and Babba heard someone puttering around in the kitchen. They heard the clatter of the dishes, and they heard someone humming, and they heard the whistling of the teakettle, and finally, when they could not be quiet one second more, both bears jumped out of bed and shouted, "Who is it? Who is in our kitchen?"

Raccoon was so startled that he dropped the
bowls he had been putting back on the shelf.
When Bubba and Babba saw their friend and the
broken bowls, they both sat down and laughed
for a long time.

Finally Babba said, "We are two silly bears. I am starving and I have never been so bored in all my life."

And Bubba said, "I have a headache and have never had so many bad dreams in all my life. Let us both try not to be so lazy anymore."

Then they all sat down and had some breakfast, which was silly because it was already dinnertime.

Tales of Long Ago

For hundreds and hundreds of years, storytellers have entertained people with these tales. You can enjoy them today and become a storyteller, too.

The Magic Brush

Traditional

Ma Liang was a boy who wanted to paint pictures more than anything else in the world. But he was very poor. He had no mother or father, so he had to take care of himself. While the other children went to school, Ma Liang gathered firewood. All he ever got for his hard work was a little money or a bowl of rice. At the end of every long day, Ma Liang was so tired that he cried himself to sleep.

One day, when the sun was very hot and his load of wood was getting heavy, Ma Liang said to himself, "I am a poor boy who cannot go to school. But it costs nothing to look at the birds in the sky or the fish in the river. I am going to learn how to paint them," he decided.

As soon as Ma Liang had finished his work, he practised drawing pictures with his finger in the sand. Then he went into his hut and found a stick that had been burned black in the fire. He used the stick to draw pictures on the wall of his hut.

From that day on, Ma Liang spent every evening drawing beautiful pictures. He drew birds swooping like kites, leaves dancing in the wind, and fish splashing in the sunny river. He practised and practised until the things he drew seemed to come alive. But they were still only charcoal figures on the walls of his poor hut.

Then one night Ma Liang had a dream. In the dream he saw an old man wearing a splendid robe made of all the colours of the world. In his hand the old man held a golden paintbrush.

"Ma Liang," said the old man in the dream. "I have been watching you draw, and I think you are ready to paint. I have brought you a magic brush. Use it wisely."

In the morning, Ma Liang woke up and found that he was holding the golden paintbrush in his hand. He jumped up and began to paint a wonderful bird of blues and greens and yellows. And then, as Ma Liang watched in amazement, the painted bird became a real bird and flew out through the open door.

For hours, Ma Liang painted all the things he loved about the world. He painted soft, smiling cats and lazy, green turtles. He painted butterflies and lizards and big, golden beetles. Everything he painted became alive and left the hut in a fantastic parade.

The next day, Ma Liang went from hut to hut with his magic paintbrush in his hand.

"What is the thing that you want most of all?" he asked the villagers. "Is it something to eat? I will paint it for you."

The people laughed at Ma Liang. "We cannot eat a painting," they said.

"Tell me what you want," Ma Liang replied. "Then wait and see what happens."

On the wall of each hut, Ma Liang painted with his magic brush. He painted rice and fish to eat, and new clothes to wear. He painted bowls and platters, soft beds, and warm blankets. Everything that he painted became real.

The poor people of the village were very surprised and very, very happy. They had everything they had ever wanted. They knew that Ma Liang had brought them a special gift, and they did not become greedy.

Ma Liang was the happiest of them all. He painted pictures all day long, and at night his dreams were filled with colour.

How the Finch Got Her Colours

Traditional

Once upon a time, when the world was new, all the birds were grey. They had no colour at all.

One day, the King of the Birds looked around him. He saw that everything in the world had colour, except the birds. He called the birds together and showed them a rainbow shimmering with red, yellow, blue, green, and purple.

"It's time I gave each of you a colour," he said. "Any colour you choose will be yours."

The grey birds were excited. They began pushing and shoving to get close to the King of the Birds.

"I'm first," yelled the parrot. "I'll take green."

"I want blue," screamed the blue jay. "Give me blue."

"Red! Red!" squawked the cardinal. "Make me red."

"Yellow is my favourite colour," chirped the canary. "I want to be yellow."

"Purple, purple, purple!" shouted the martin. "Give me purple."

The King of the Birds gave out the colours as quickly as he could. Soon, all the colours were gone. The birds flew away to look at themselves in a nearby pond.

Just then, the King of the Birds noticed a little, grey finch sitting on a branch. "Why didn't you come with the others when I gave out the colours?" he asked.

"I was waiting for my turn," said the finch. "Now all the colours are gone. I will be grey forever."

"That wouldn't be fair," said the King of the Birds.

The King of the Birds called all the birds back from the pond. He told them to hop slowly past him. From each bird he took back a tiny bit of colour. He took some red from the cardinal, some blue from the blue jay, some green from the parrot, some yellow from the canary, and some purple from the martin. He gave all the colours he had gathered to the finch.

The little finch glimmered in the sun with all the colours of the rainbow.

One jealous bird asked the King of the Birds why he had given the finch so many colours.

The King of the Birds said to them, "While all of you screamed and yelled and pushed and shoved, the little finch waited her turn. It is only fair that she should have more colours than any of you."

Everything Has a History

Am I old? Am I new?
Did I just grow? Or was I invented?
What is my history?

Let's Make a Museum!

Mrs. Carpenter's Plan

On Monday morning, Mrs. Carpenter said to her students, "We're going to do something different this week. We're going to make a museum."

Mrs. Carpenter reached inside a box and lifted out a small, wooden boat. "My great-grandfather made this boat a long time ago," she said. "The sails are made of tusk. People don't hunt animals for their tusks anymore, but at one time tusks were used for many things."

Mrs. Carpenter held up the sailboat so everyone could see it. "This boat has its very own history," she continued. "So does everything you see around you."

"Now do you know how we're going to make our own museum?" asked Mrs. Carpenter.

"I do," said Anne. "We'll all bring in old things from home."

"Well," said Mrs. Carpenter, "you can bring in old things if you want to. But remember, *everything* has a history. No matter what you choose, you'll be collecting little bits of history. When you go home today, look around your house. Ask your parents what special thing you could bring in for our museum."

What Should We Bring?

In school the next day, the children talked about what they might bring in.

Mrs. Carpenter listened to them, then she asked, "How are we going to decide what each of you will bring? Think about our trip to the museum last week. Some things were made by hand, some were made by nature, and some were made by machines."

"I know what we can do," said Frank. "We can make a chart."

"That's a good idea," said Mrs. Carpenter. "Now let's get started."

Setting Up the Museum

The next morning, the children brought in their special things.

Mrs. Carpenter had cleared a large table at the back of the room. "This is where we'll set up our museum," she said. "When everything is arranged, each of you can write about what you've brought."

The children worked together to set up their museum. Mrs. Carpenter helped them write something about their special objects. When they were finished, there was a card for each object in the museum.

A Very Old Horn

by Carl

I found this old horn in my grandfather's barn. I stepped on it and it honked so loud that I jumped! I polished it, and it got so shiny that I gave it to my dad. He took it to his office. I don't think he honks it much there!

My Sailboat Painting

by Anne

I like sailboats. Mine's in a painting. It's so small because it was part of an old, wooden door. My mother likes the painting because it's one of a kind. But I like it mostly because of the sailboat.

My Grandfather's Toy Car

by Ameera

My grandfather saved some of the toys he had when he was little. They are very old. My favourite is this toy car. It has a spring that makes it go. My grandfather let me bring it in for the museum.

My Ocean Collection

by Robert

These are some of the things I found when I was in Nova Scotia last summer. Well, the blowfish is really from Mexico. My uncle brought it back from his holidays there. But it's from the ocean, too, so I keep it with my shells.

The children set up the objects and put the cards in place. At last, the museum was ready. Mrs. Carpenter invited the whole school to visit it. Everyone enjoyed seeing the museum and discovering that everything has a history. It wasn't long before other classes made museums of their own.

Wonderful Ways to Go

You can travel anywhere
you want to go,
riding on your imagination.

Ride Your Imagination

You can ride on the back of a camel,
You can swing on a rope through the trees,
You can hop in a kangaroo's pocket,
You can travel however you please.

Of course you can be an inventor,
And think up a super machine
That rattles and buzzes and whistles
And takes you where you've never been.

You can travel wherever you want to—
Over land, under sea, in the air.
You can use your imagination
And you're suddenly, magically there.

The
Happy Wanderers

by John E. McCormack

On a warm summer day, Rabbit and Hare sat in the shade of a willow tree, watching the river flow past.

"I have an idea," said Hare. "Let's build a raft."

"I'd rather build a clubhouse," said Rabbit.

"A RAFT!" cried Hare.

"A CLUBHOUSE!" shouted Rabbit.

Rabbit stamped off upstream.

Hare marched into the forest.

Rabbit found a large wooden box behind a supermarket.

"This box is as big as a house," he said.

Rabbit put his roller skates under the box. Then, pushing with all his strength, he rolled it down to the river.

Rabbit rushed home for his tools.

Meanwhile, Hare found some long, round logs in the forest.

"These are just what I need," he said.

Hare rolled the logs down to the river's edge. Then he hurried home for his tools.

Rabbit sawed and hammered. He put a roof on the box. He cut out doors and windows. He put in bunk beds, a wood stove, and a bathtub.

"A wonderful job, Rabbit!" cried a voice from the river. "How do you like the raft I made?"

Rabbit was impressed. "That's no ordinary raft," he cried.

"Indeed not," said Hare proudly. "It's complete with a paddle wheel, steering wheel, pedals, and a horn." *Toot-toot!* "And it's built for speed."

Rabbit looked at the raft. Then he looked at the clubhouse.

Hare looked at the clubhouse. Then he looked at the raft.

"Are you thinking what I'm thinking?" asked Rabbit.

"Yes," said Hare. "Let's get busy."

"Now we have our very own riverboat," said Rabbit a while later.

Hare nailed a sign over the cabin door.

The sign read: The Happy Wanderer.

Rabbit and Hare moved in that day.

Then they pedalled off downstream, singing a riverboat song.

"Yo ho! Yo ho-o-o! A riverboater's life for me."

Brendan, Morgan and the Best Ever Cloud Machine

by Gerrem Evans

One sunny morning Brendan and Morgan watched a cloud drifting above them in the sky. They watched it change shape from a ball to a fish to a horse.

Brendan decided he wanted to be like a cloud, to change shape and float over mountains and rivers and see wonderful things on land and sea.

"But," Brendan said to himself, "clouds don't have bones. How can I be like a cloud if I have bones?"

"Morgan," he said to his little brother, "look like you don't have bones," and Morgan obligingly collapsed to the ground.

Morgan practised being as quiet as a cloud while Brendan frowned and thought and pondered and speculated.

Then Brendan formed a plan. He wanted a cloud that would fly. It had to look like a cloud outside and have a machine inside, so he could sit and control the cloud's movements. He wanted it to go up and down, and left and right.

First, he found a bench and a platform to put the bench on.

"Morgan," Brendan asked, "help me. Go up the hill and catch a cloud. I want to see what it looks like up close."

Morgan ran off to catch a cloud.

Then, after Brendan had hammered and sawed and nailed and glued most of the cloud machine together, Morgan came back with a sad face and an empty pot.

"Never mind, Morgan, you can do something else," Brendan said.

So, before Brendan attached some balloons around the edge of the platform to lift up their cloud machine, Morgan sat on the strings to make sure they didn't escape.

Then Brendan made some squirters. The squirters would control the shape of the cloud. The hot air squirter would make the cloud bigger and the cold air squirter would make the cloud smaller.

Soon Brendan and Morgan were ready to climb aboard. And up they zoomed, up, up, up, up!

Trees flew by. Birds stopped in mid-air squawking and flapping. Brendan grinned, held his breath and concentrated on the squirters. Morgan gasped and laughed and hung on to his seat belt.

There was a lurch and a slide.

Then everything jumped and bumped and began to wobble. It was a jerky, lumpy wobble. Somehow the button controls didn't work very well. The wind was too strong and pushed the platform right when Brendan wanted to go left and straight ahead when he wanted to go back.

Brendan pushed buttons and squished squirters until his face was red. He had a lopsided cloud going nowhere.

Down they came very fast and very bumpily.

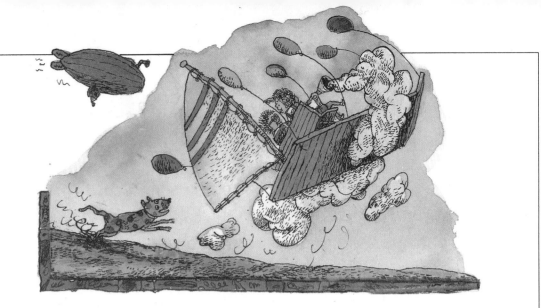

Brendan sat and he frowned. Morgan lay beside him, closed one eye and rested just a little bit. Brendan thought and he pondered and he speculated. At last he had an idea. He needed a sail. He borrowed a sheet from his bed, found a pole for a mast and fastened it beside the bench on the platform.

"Come on Morgan, let's go," Brendan said.

Morgan opened his eye, stared for a moment at the sky, then pointed.

"Yes, I see it, that black thing," said Brendan. "But there aren't any clouds. We'll have the whole sky to ourselves."

Brendan and Morgan clambered onto the platform. Brendan pushed the UP button and off they zoomed again, up, up, up!

Brendan set the sail and pushed his buttons and squished his squirters. Brendan zigged and Morgan zagged as they flew around the sky. Brendan squished the hot steamy air and Morgan squished the cold icy air. And between them they created a magnificent cloud.

But on one of the zags, Morgan grabbed his brother's arm and pointed over his shoulder.

Looming, and rushing toward them from behind, was a huge, black machine. Brendan saw the printed words, "DIRIGIBLE—CLOUD DISPERSER." He jabbed the UP button and shouted, "Morgan get down!"

They saw spurts of orangy yellow, like liquid sun rays, evaporate part of their cloud.

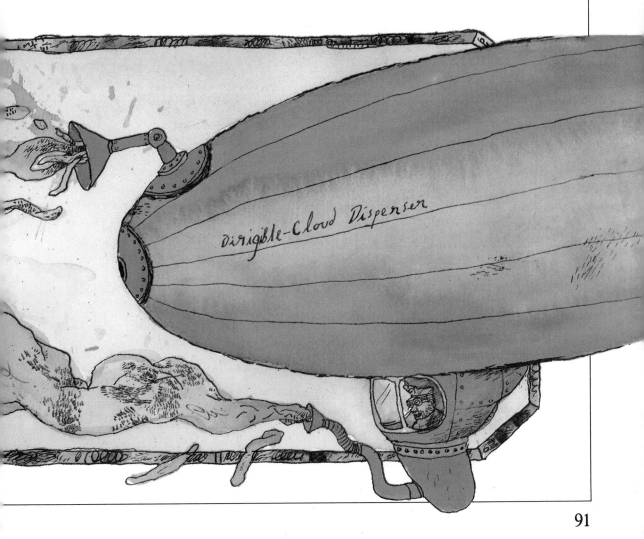

There was a crash as the nose of the Dirigible
butted under the platform of the Cloud Machine.
Brendan and Morgan slithered and slid, then
wedged against a funnel on top of the Dirigible.

The sail was askew, the mast atilt. Morgan's
seat was broken. He closed his eyes and bellowed,
"I want to go home. Now."

Brendan peered carefully over the edge. He
put his arm around Morgan's shoulders. "Don't
worry. Don't worry, we just have to fix a few
things. You sit on the funnel and hang on to the
Cloud Machine while I see if the squirters work."

Brendan straightened the mast, re-set the sail, roped the seat together and checked the squirters. The balloons were intact.

Then Brendan aimed the hot steamy squirter at the port holes on both sides of the Dirigible. The portholes fogged over. No one could see out and the Dirigible pointed toward the earth.

Brendan and Morgan jumped on the Cloud Machine and climbed quickly skyward.

Below them they could see where the Dirigible had landed in a thicket of trees. And way down below, very faintly, Brendan heard voices from a crowd.

"Is it a cloud?"

"Is it a Martian ship?"

"Maybe it's a magic cloud."

"Oh me, oh my, what a peculiar cloud."

"Who could make such a marvellous cloud?"

And away up there, Brendan shouted, "Me! Me! I did. I did. Me and Morgan did."

Brendan and Morgan waved to the people below.

Brendan grinned at his brother and said, "Did you notice, we are the only cloud in the sky? We have the best ever cloud. And we can go home now if you want."

Morgan nodded.

"What do you want to do after dinner?" asked Brendan.

"Dunno," Morgan said.

"Let's build a submarine!" said Brendan.

The End.

Project Manager: Christine Anderson
Senior Editor: Jocelyn Van Huyse
Contributing Writer: Lauren Wolk
Series Design: Rob McPhail and Lorraine Tuson
Design and Art Direction: Lorraine Tuson
Associate Designer: Donald Gauthier
Cover Design: Taylor/Levkoe Associates Limited
Cover Illustration: Mark Craig
Typesetting: Trigraph Inc.
Printing: The Bryant Press Limited

Acknowledgements

All selections in this book have been written or adapted by John McInnes and John Ryckman, with the exception of the following:

Sidewalk Super: From SUBWAY SWINGER by Virginia Schonborg. Copyright © by Virginia Schonborg. By permission of William Morrow & Company.

The First Time I Heard Snow: by Lauren Wolk.

Bubba and Babba: Reprinted from BUBBA AND BABBA by Maria Polushkin Robbins. Copyright © 1975 by Crown Juvenile. Used by permission of Crown Juvenile.

The Magic Brush: Traditional

How the Finch Got Her Colours: Traditional

The Happy Wanderers: Adapted from RABBIT TRAVELS by John E. McCormack, illustrated by Lynne Cherry. Text copyright © 1984 by John E. McCormack. Illustrations copyright © 1984 by Lynne Cherry. Reprinted by permission of the publisher, E. P. Dutton, a division of New American Library.

Brendan, Morgan and the Best Ever Cloud Machine: Reprinted from BRENDAN, MORGAN AND THE BEST EVER CLOUD MACHINE by Gerrem Evans. Copyright © 1985 by Gerrem Evans. Used by permission of Annick Press.

Illustrations

Lynne Cherry: 76-82; Mark Craig: 5, 25, 49, 63, 73; Henrik Drescher: 83-95; Laura Fernandez: 18-24; Sharon Foster: 58-62; Donald Gauthier: 10-15, 16-17; Wojtek Gorczynski: 35-39; Peter Kovalik: 6-9; Glenn Mielke: 40-48; Maureen Paxton: 74-75; Lorraine Tuson: 50-57

Photographs

M. Beedell/Miller Services: 29; Camerique/Miller Services: 27; Kenneth W. Fink/Ardea London Ltd: 30 (bottom), 32 (top and bottom), 33, 34 (top and bottom); Jacob Formsma/Network Stock Photo File: 30 (top); Francois Gohier/Ardea London Ltd.: 26 (right); Barry Griffiths/Network Stock Photo File: 31; Martin W. Grosnick/Ardea London Ltd.: 26 (left); James D. Markou: Miller Services: 28 (top); John E. Swedberg/Ardea London Ltd.: 28 (bottom)

5 6 7 8 9 0 BP 6 5 4 3 2 1 0 9